A Note to Parents

DK READERS is a compelling programme for beginning readers, designed in conjunction with leading literacy experts, including Maureen Fernandes. B.Ed (hons). Maureen has spent many years teaching literacy, both in the classroom and as a consultant in schools.

Beautiful illustrations and superb full-colour photographs combine with engaging, easy-to-read stories to offer a fresh approach to each subject in the series. Each DK READER is guaranteed to capture a child's interest while developing his or her reading skills, general knowledge and love of reading.

The five levels of DK READERS are aimed at different reading abilities, enabling you to choose the books that are exactly right for your child:

Pre-level 1: Learning to read
Level 1: Beginning to read
Level 2: Beginning to read alone
Level 3: Reading alone
Level 4: Proficient readers

The "normal" age at which a child begins to read can be anywhere from three to eight years old. Adult participation through the lower levels is very helpful for providing encouragement, discussing storylines, and sounding out unfamiliar words.

No matter which level you select, you can be sure that you are helping your child learn to read, then read to learn!

LONDON, NEW YORK, MUNICH,
MELBOURNE, AND DELHI

For Dorling Kindersley
Managing Art Editor Ron Stobbart
Publishing Manager Catherine Saunders
Art Director Lisa Lanzarini
Publisher Simon Beecroft
Publishing Director Alex Allan
Production Editor Marc Staples
Production Controller Kara Wallace
Reading Consultant Maureen Fernandes

For Lucasfilm
Executive Editor J. W. Rinzler
Art Director Troy Alders
Keeper of the Holocron Leland Chee
Director of Publishing Carol Roeder

Designed and edited by Tall Tree Ltd
Designer Ben Ruocco
Editor Jon Richards

First published in Great Britain in 2012 by
Dorling Kindersley Limited
80 Strand, London WC2R 0RL

12 13 14 15 16 10 9 8 7 6 5 4 3 2 1

001—182942—05/12

A CIP catalogue record for this book
is available from the British Library

ISBN: 9781409383208

Printed and bound in China by L. Rex Printing Company Ltd

Discover more at
www.dk.com
www.starwars.com

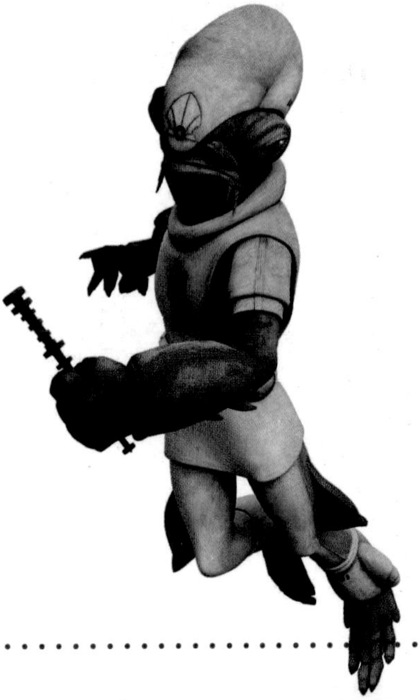

DK READERS

READING 3 ALONE

STAR WARS™

THE CLONE WARS™

Ackbar's Underwater Army

Written by Simon Beecroft

Crisis under the waves

During the deadly Clone Wars, one far-away planet has problems of its own.

This world, called Mon Calamari, is covered with oceans. Its people live in cities beneath the waves.

On Mon Calamari, many different species live in harmony – or at least they used to.

One species, the Mon Cala, are amphibians with fish-like heads. These peaceful and clever aliens build the best starships in the galaxy.

The Clone Wars

After generations of peace, the Galactic Republic is now at war. In the Clone Wars, the Separatists, led by Count Dooku, want to take over the galaxy.

Another species, the squid-like Quarren, are rivals to the Mon Cala. The Quarren generally live away from the Mon Cala in cities on the sea bed, but now they have emerged from the depths.

The trouble began with a brutal event. The Mon Cala king Yos Kolina was found mysteriously murdered. The next in line to the throne is his young son, Prince Lee-Char. But is Lee-Char ready to be king?

The Mon Cala and the Quarren leaders meet to discuss the matter.

Prince Lee-Char is Yos Kolina's young son. He wants to prove to his people that he can be a good ruler.

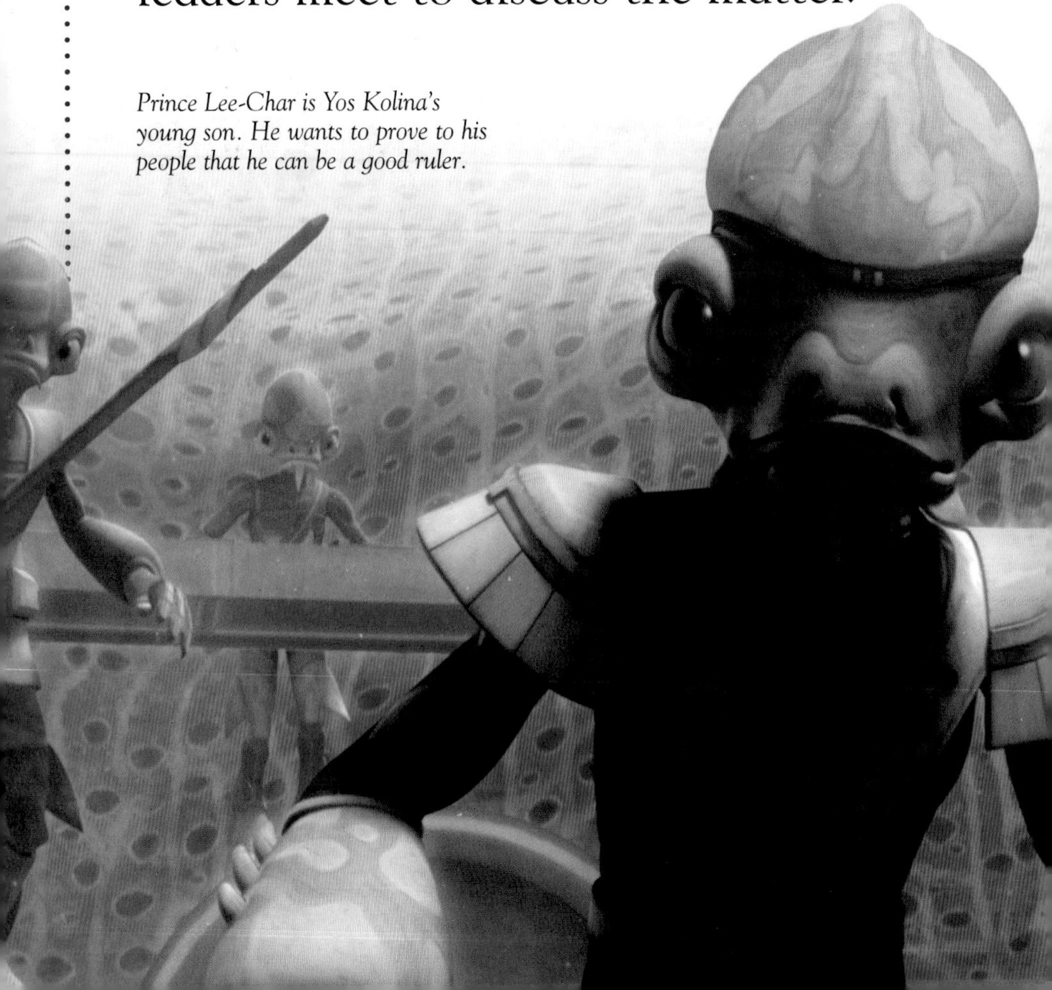

The Quarren leader is a respected chieftain called Nossor Ri. He supported Yos Kolina, but he thinks Prince Lee-Char is too young to rule. Now Nossor Ri wants a Quarren king!

Respected Ruler

King Yos Kolina was the 82nd king of the Mon Cala. He was a brave leader who worked hard to keep the peace between his own species and the Quarren.

Prince Lee-Char realises he needs to prove himself. Luckily, he has a loyal supporter: Captain Ackbar. This gruff military leader is captain of the Mon Calamari Guard and was chief adviser to King Yos Kolina.

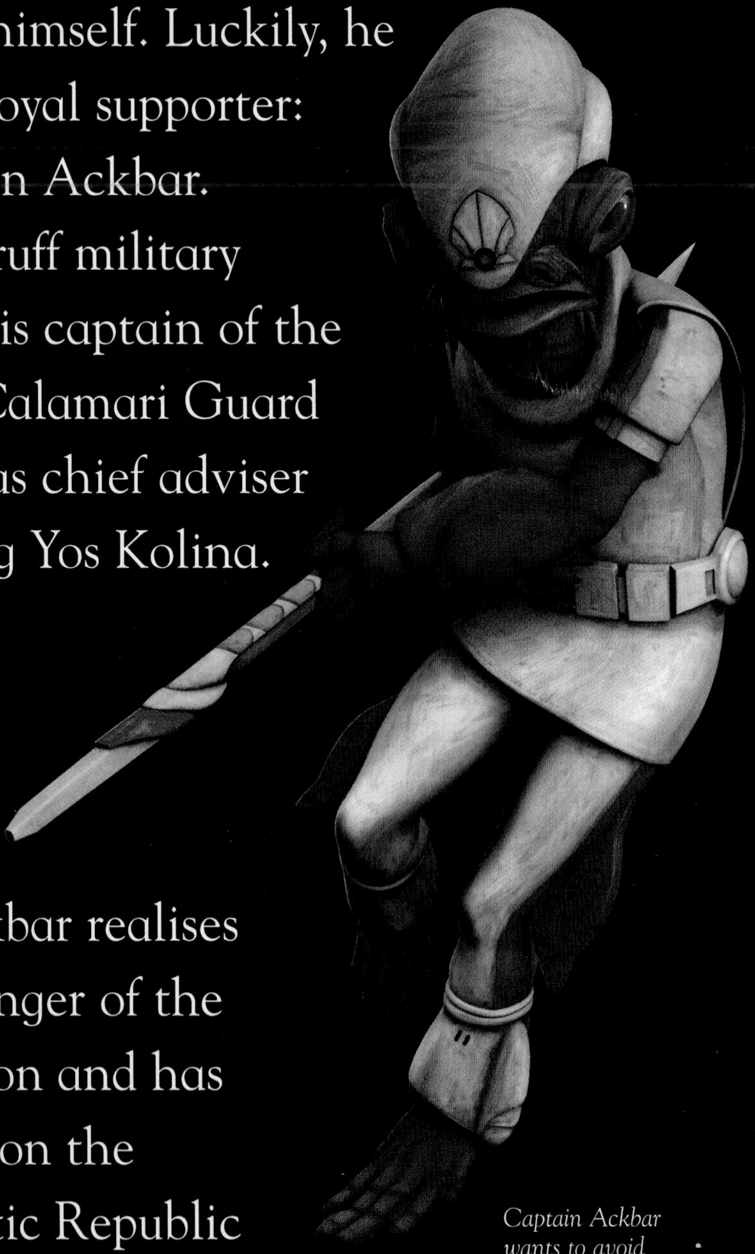

Ackbar realises the danger of the situation and has called on the Galactic Republic for help.

Captain Ackbar wants to avoid a war with the Quarren.

Help arrives in the form of Senator Padmé Amidala, accompanied by her Jedi bodyguard, Anakin Skywalker.

The Quarren have also called for help. They have sided with the Separatists. The Separatists send one of their most feared warriors to the planet: a shark-headed monster called Riff Tamson.

Republic Defenders

Padmé Amidala is loyal to the Galactic Republic and wants to restore peace to the galaxy. Anakin is a warrior monk called a Jedi. He receives special powers from a mystical energy called the Force.

Riff Tamson is a Karkarodon. His huge mouth is full of sharp teeth.

Tamson takes orders from the villainous Separatist leader, Count Dooku. He does not want a peaceful solution to the crisis on Mon Calamari. Tamson wants war and he's brought his own army.

In battle, Riff Tamson bites and destroys opponents with his strong teeth.

Is Riff Tamson really here to help the Quarren put one of their own kind on the throne?

Or are he and Count Dooku secretly scheming to take control of the planet for the Separatists?

What do you think?

Riff Tamson commands an army of deadly Aqua Droids. The droids are armed and dangerous. Tamson and his army head towards the Mon Cala city.

Tamson gives the command to attack! Captain Ackbar is ready to defend the city. But he must also look after Prince Lee-Char.

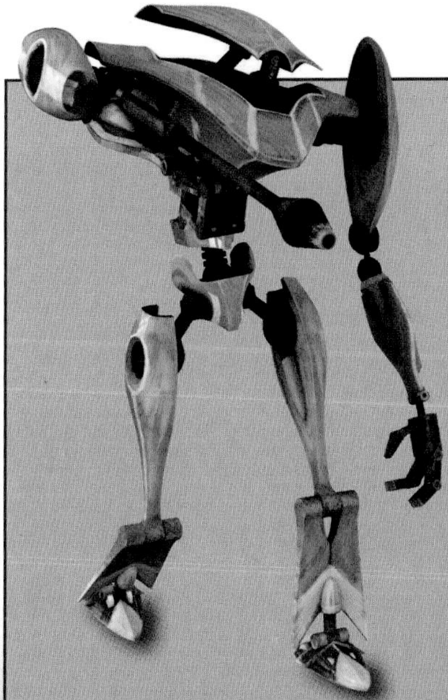

Underwater droids

Aqua Droids can operate on land and underwater. They are equipped with a powerful laser cannon attached to one arm. Their feet become propellers when they are swimming underwater.

Riff Tamson leads his Aqua Droid soldiers into battle. He thinks the war will be quick and easy to win.

Captain Ackbar is in a difficult position. Lee-Char is Supreme Commander of the Mon Cala army, so Ackbar must follow his command. But Lee-Char has never led an army before. He does not know about battle tactics. Even so, he's determined to give it his best try.

The Prince tells Ackbar that the Quarren won't attack. But they do attack. He commands Ackbar to stay with him at the edge of the battlefield. But, without Ackbar at the front, his army starts losing. Lee-Char realises that he should allow Ackbar to advise him. He finally lets Ackbar join his men in battle.

Ackbar is determined to show Lee-Char how to lead an army.

The Mon Calamari Guard serves the king of the planet. Under Ackbar's leadership, the Guard is one of the best fighting forces in the galaxy. Mon Cala soldiers wear simple armour. They are armed with spear blasters. These weapons fire bolts of deadly energy from one end.

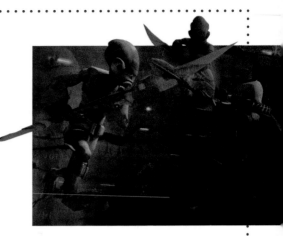

They can also be flipped round and used as a fighting spear for close combat.

Ackbar's army can hold back the Quarren soldiers – but it cannot hold back the Aqua Droids for ever.

Captain Ackbar leads his Mon Calamari Guard into battle against the Quarren.

All-Out War!

Ahsoka

With the battle becoming fierce, the Mon Cala realise they need reinforcements.

The Republic sends SCUBA clones, along with two Jedi Knights: Kit Fisto and Ahsoka Tano.

Kit Fisto

The SCUBA clones fly in with all guns blazing. In a break from the battle, Ackbar tries to inspire Prince Lee-Char to be brave. He says if his people see his bravery, they will respect him. He hands Lee-Char a rifle and tells him to "lead!"

Prince Lee-Char picks up a rifle for the first time. He must lead his soldiers!

SCUBA clones

These elite SCUBA clone troopers wear watertight armour with aquatic propulsion backpacks and flipper feet. They are specially trained for underwater combat.

Before Lee-Char has a chance to prove himself, he has a nasty surprise. In a flash, Riff Tamson appears. With lightning-fast Jedi reflexes, Ahsoka grabs hold of Lee-Char and zips him away on a Jedi sub.

Tamson gives chase, his jaws snapping at their heels. Just when Ahsoka and Lee-Char think they'll be eaten, Mon Cala soldiers arrive. They fire at Tamson and force him to abandon his attack. They are safe for now. But for how long?

Jedi sub
The Republic uses vehicles called OMS Devilfish Subs. They are armed with blaster cannons.

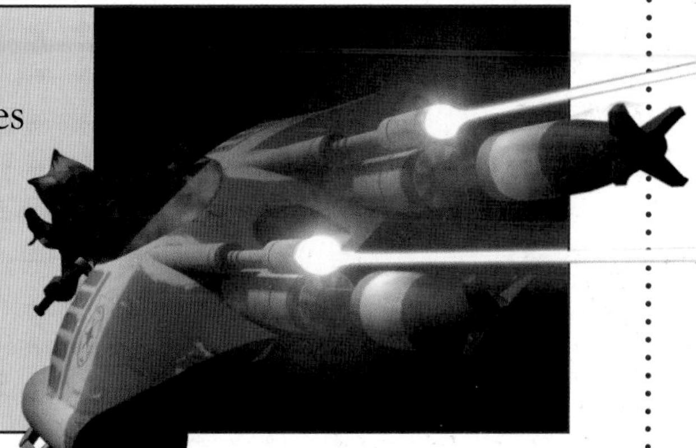

Meanwhile, back at the battlefront, Ackbar and the underwater army have forced the droids to retreat. But Riff Tamson has some secret weapons: Hydroid Medusas. These huge jellyfish are half machine, half monster. They move towards Captain Ackbar, Prince Lee-Char and the Jedi. Their tentacles are crackling with electricity. One touch can kill!

Jellyfish Weapons
Hydroid Medusas were developed on Tamson's home world, Karkaris. Their large electrified tentacles can kill anyone who touches them.

This time, Lee-Char is determined to be a good leader. He orders his troops to fire at the Medusas. But the Medusas are too powerful. Ackbar knows that they must pull back if they want to live to fight another day. Lee-Char is learning that there's a time to fight and be brave – and a time to retreat.

The Mon Cala and their allies look on in horror as the Hydroid Medusas destroy all in their path.

Ackbar and the Jedi ask for the advice of top Jedi commanders, Yoda and Mace Windu. The Jedi decide to request help from the Grand Army of the Gungans.

Medusa jellyfish have surrounded Ackbar, Anakin and Padmé. They know they have no defence against the Medusas.

Suddenly, something is blowing up the mechanical jellyfish. The Gungans have arrived.

Hooray for the Gungans!

The Gungans throw their booma weapons at the jellyfish, blowing them up.

Aquatic Allies

The Gungans live in the swamps and lakes of Padmé Amidala's home planet, Naboo. One of the most famous Gungans is Jar Jar Binks.

Not far away, Prince Lee-Char and Ahsoka are sadly watching the Quarren take captured Mon Cala soldiers to prisoner camps. Lee-Char must find a way to lead his people. He calls out to the captured Mon Cala prisoners: "You will not be prisoners much longer!"

They call back to him: "We will fight for you, Prince!"

These words give Lee-Char courage. He grabs a blaster rifle and joins the battle to free the prisoners.

Finally, the Mon Cala are fighting back against their Quarren captors. But Tamson has another surprise for our heroes. He barks an order to his Quarren crew: "Churn them up!"

Lee-Char is growing up quickly, and finds the courage to fight back against the Quarren.

A menacing, dark shadow appears above the defenders of Mon Calamari. Lee-Char and the others look up to see gigantic Trident Drills moving down towards them. The Drills begin to turn like massive propellers. They create huge waves in the underwater world. The destructive current pulls our heroes around.

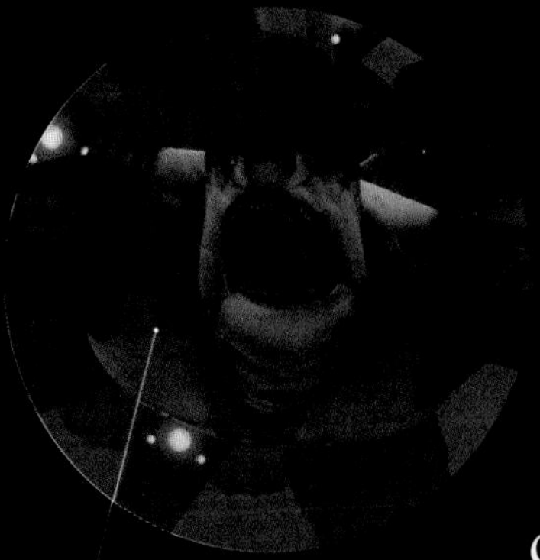

Riff Tamson

But there is worse. The bottom of a Trident Drill opens up, and Riff Tamson comes flying out. Tamson heads straight for the Prince. His jaws are wide open, showing rows of deadly teeth.

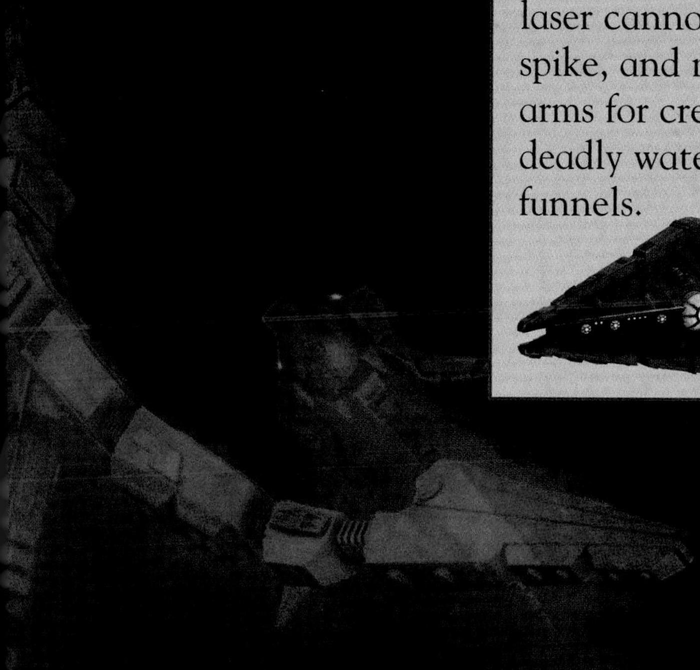

The Trident ships spin their arms, making powerful waves.

Drill ship
Trident Drills have laser cannons, a drill spike, and mechanical arms for creating deadly water funnels.

Tamson's jaws snap at the Prince. Just as Tamson is about to bite, Kit Fisto leaps at him. He lands a fist on the creature's jaw. Fisto shouts to Ahsoka, "Escape with the Prince, I'll hold him off!" Ahsoka and the Prince escape. But Tamson's droids quickly surround Fisto, along with Anakin, Padmé, and Jar Jar Binks. He has captured them all!

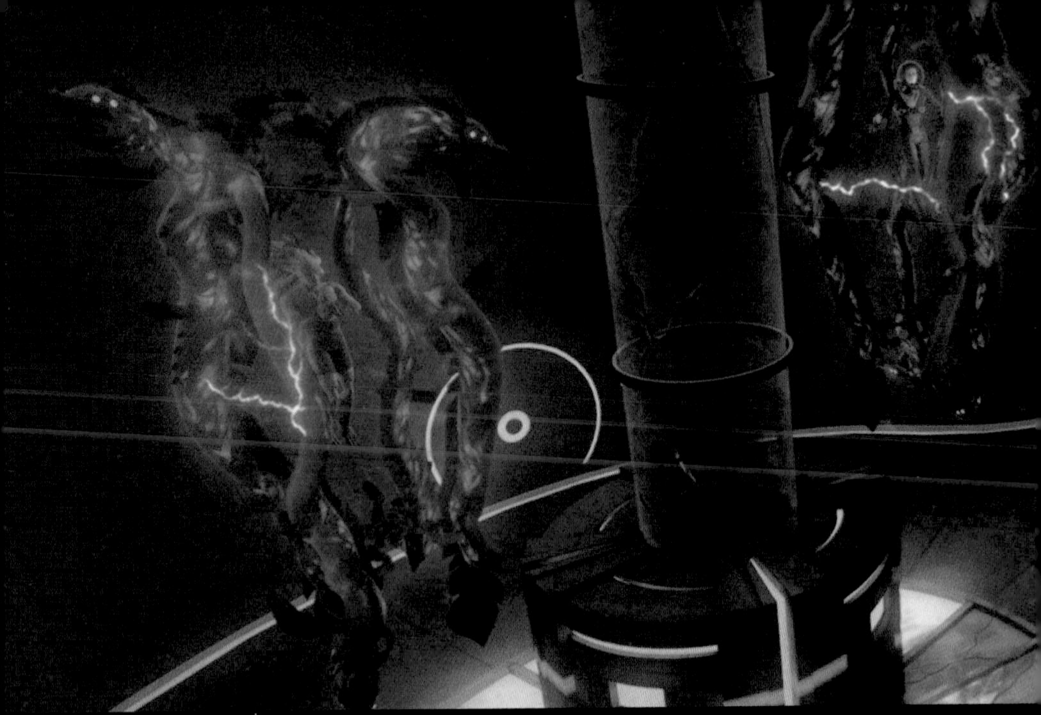

Final Showdown

Mon Calamari appears to be in Riff Tamson's evil grasp. Ackbar is being held in a prison camp. Anakin, Padmé, Kit Fisto and Jar Jar Binks are Tamson's personal captives.

Tamson's guards lock Padmé and Jar Jar into a crab trap. Tamson puts the Jedi Knights Anakin and Kit Fisto inside eel chambers. The eels are crackling with electricity.

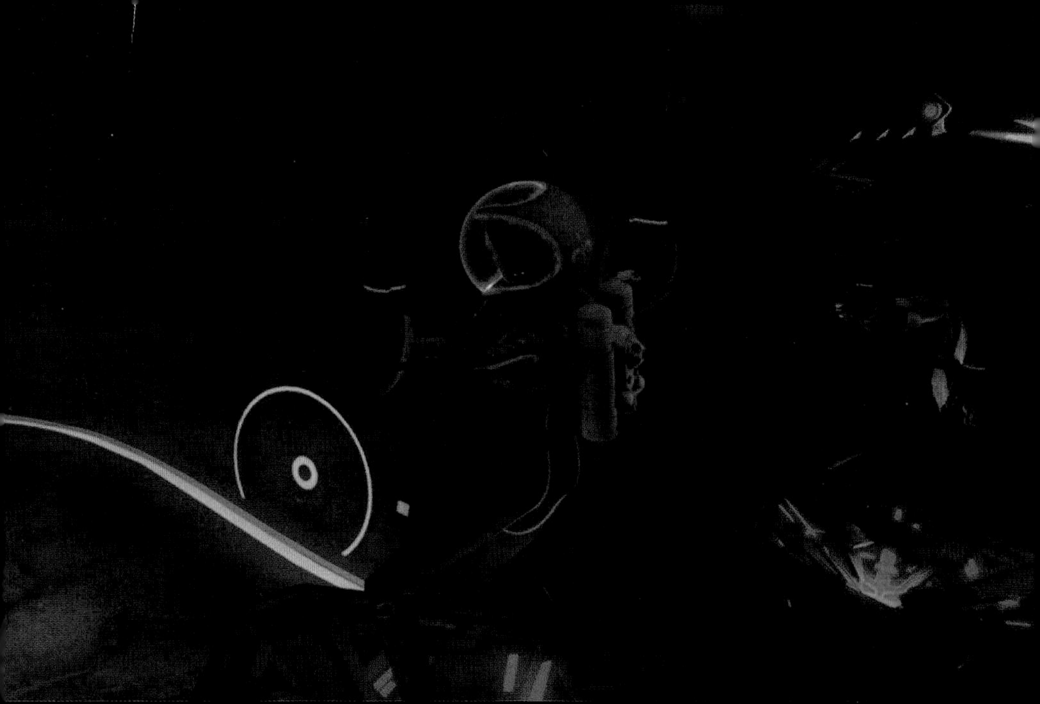

Riff Tamson has captured all of our brave heroes!

Riff Tamson speaks to Anakin: "Tell me where is Prince Lee-Char?" Anakin says nothing. A guard pokes one of the eels with his weapon. The eel electrocutes the Jedi.

After hiding in the coral, Lee-Char and Ahsoka sneak into a Quarren prison camp. The Mon Cala prisoners are inspired by seeing the Prince. Then the Prince spots the person he is looking for: Captain Ackbar!

Ackbar is injured and has given up hope. Now it is Lee-Char's turn to help Ackbar. He tells him that they can win! They need to make the Quarren realise that Tamson is tricking them. He only wants the throne for himself!

Ackbar finds the strength to get up and ready the soldiers to fight back!

Tamson still wants to know where the Prince is, but he cannot get answers from Anakin and Fisto, no matter how hard he tries.

Then he has another nasty idea. He swims up to Padmé. His eyes roll back and his jaw opens. He bites the glass of Padmé's helmet. The glass cracks. Padmé is horrified to see a trickle of water enter her helmet!

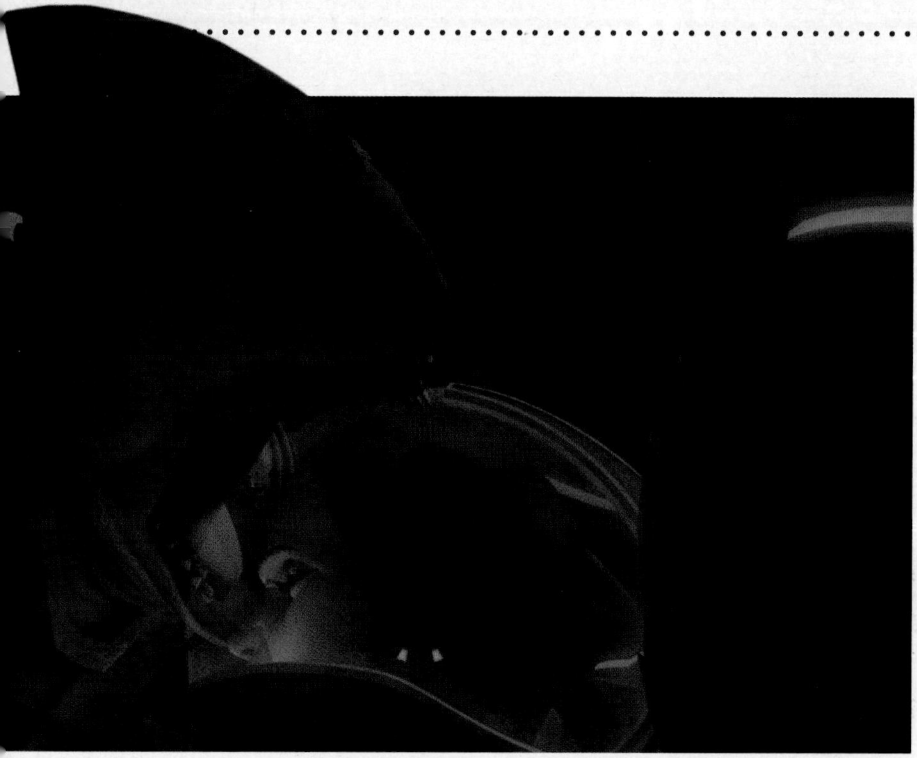

If Anakin does not tell Tamson where the Prince is hiding, Padmé will drown! But he doesn't know where the Prince is hiding!

Just then, Tamson receives a message. The Prince has given himself up. Tamson departs, leaving Padmé to drown!

Anakin tries to use the Force to keep the water from entering Padmé's helmet. But the electric eels keep jolting him, causing him to lose his concentration.

Suddenly, there is a hacking noise. Jar Jar spits goo from his mouth.

Jar Jar is being held prisoner and cannot move his arms. But he can still spit! His goo saves Padmé's life.

It hits Padmé's helmet and coats it in a sticky glob. It's disgusting but it works – the crack is sealed! Padmé will not drown inside her helmet.

Prince Lee-Char and Ahsoka are escorted into the Mon Cala throne room. Riff Tamson is sitting on the throne. He looks very pleased with himself.

Lee-Char tells Tamson he has come to demand the freedom of his people – and the freedom of the Quarren.

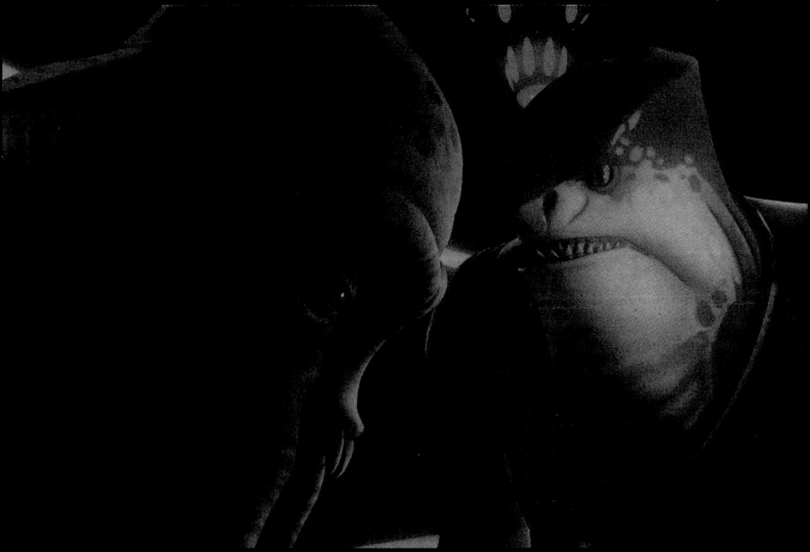

Tamson laughs at Nossor Ri, and the Quarren chieftain begins to suspect that he has been tricked.

Nossor Ri looks surprised.

Lee-Char tells Nossor Ri that the Quarren are slaves. Tamson is tricking them. They must put aside their differences and work together to make Mon Calamari whole again.

Tamson only laughs at Nossor Ri and Lee-Char. He orders the guards to take the Prince away – to his execution!

Anakin, Padmé, Kit Fisto and Jar Jar are brought in their cages to watch the execution of Prince Lee-Char. Ahsoka is already there.

The guards surround Lee-Char. Riff Tamson gives the order to execute the Prince.

Just then, everything goes dark! It is Nossor Ri and the Quarren.

They are squirting ink everywhere. They have turned against Tamson and are trying to save the Prince!

Nossor Ri squirts black ink into the water. In the confusion, the Mon Cala rise against their captors.

A massive battle erupts. Ahsoka cuts Anakin free from his eel bonds. Anakin frees Padmé and Jar Jar.

Tamson comes face to face with Lee-Char.

"I killed your father," says Tamson.

"Then I'll return the favour!" says Lee-Char. He is now a brave warrior!

Lee-Char takes aim as Riff Tamson charges at him through the murky water.

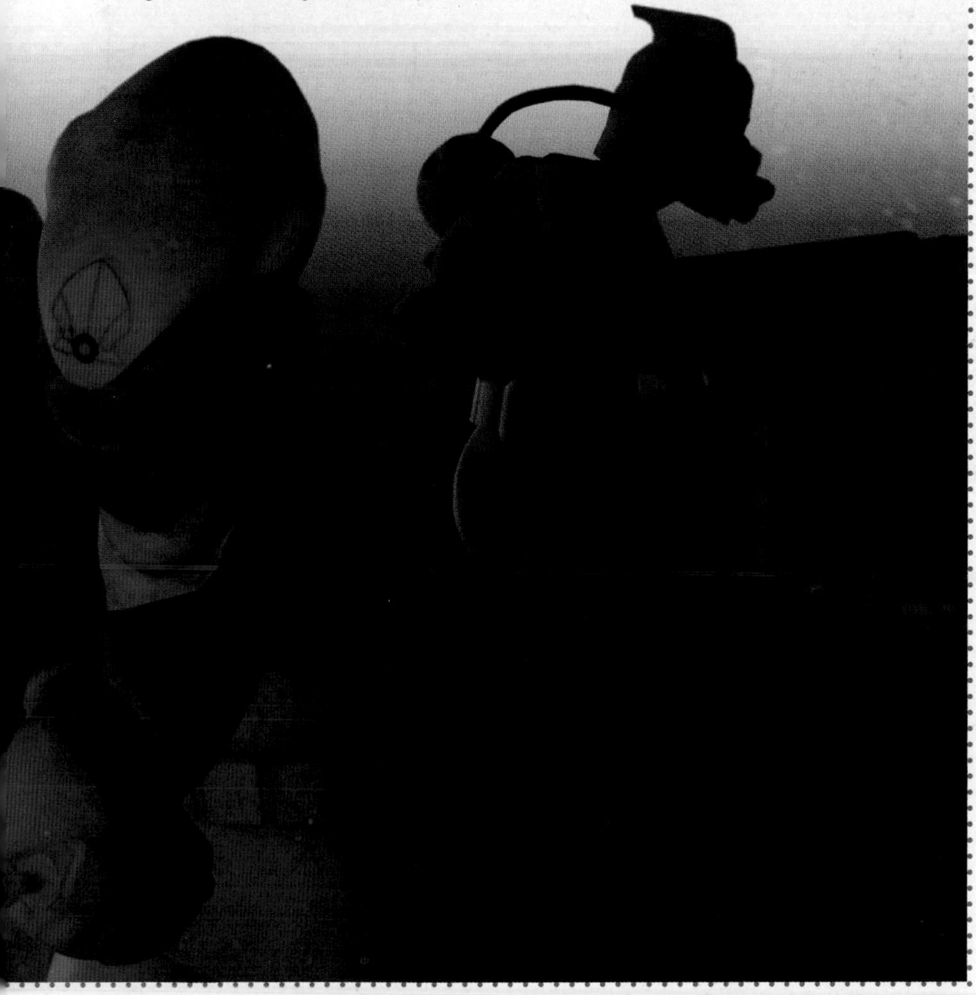

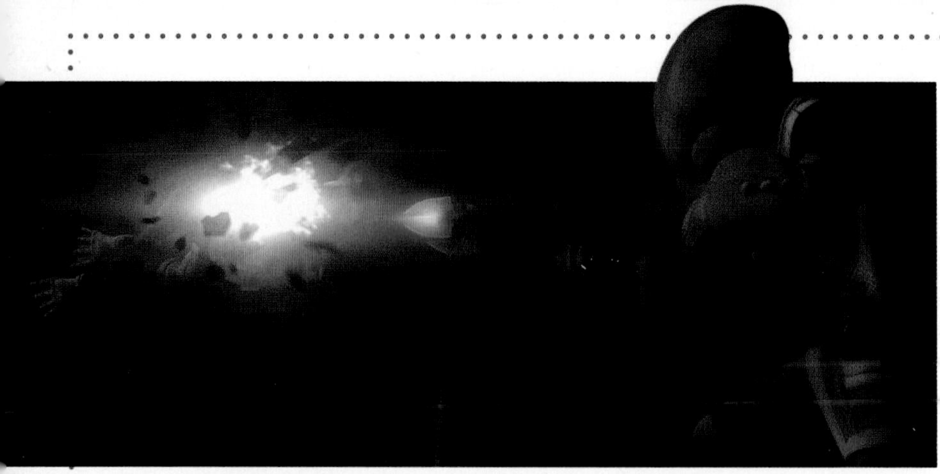

Lee-Char throws a detonator at Tamson. It sticks in his shoulder. Before the shark can reach him, Lee-Char fires his rifle and hits the detonator. Boom! Victory! Tamson is dead.

Future Rebel

This is not the last we will see of Captain Ackbar. When the Republic falls to the rule of an evil Emperor, he will join the Rebel Alliance and help defeat this hideous tyrant.

Ackbar and all his soldiers crowd around Lee-Char, saying, "Long live the Prince!" Nossor Ri pledges the loyalty of the Quarren people to him.

Lee-Char has again united the Mon Cala and the Quarren. Now he will be crowned. Long live the King, long live King Lee-Char!

Prince Lee-Char has triumphed. But he could not have done it without the help of Captain Ackbar, the Jedi and the Gungans.

Quiz

1. Is Captain Ackbar a Mon Cala or a Quarren?
2. Who murdered King Yos Kolina?
3. Which animal do Hydroid Medusas look like?
4. How does Jar Jar seal the crack in Padmé Amidala's helmet?

Put the scenes in the right order:

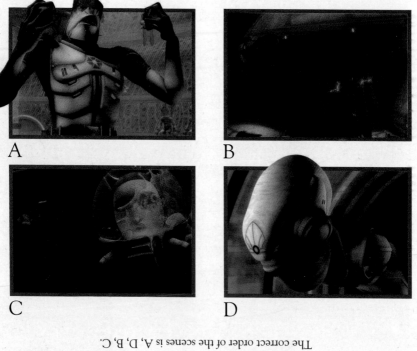

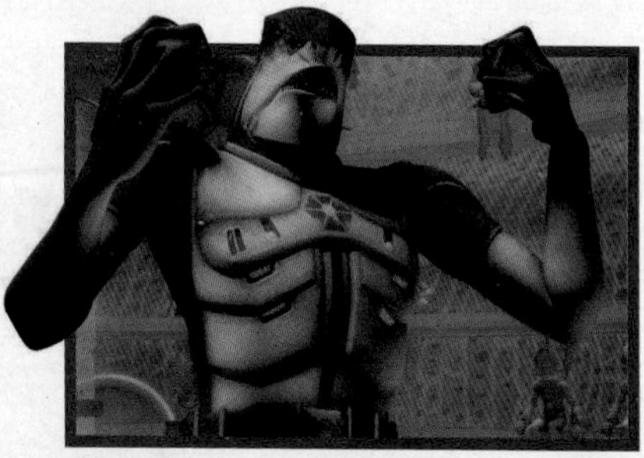
A

B

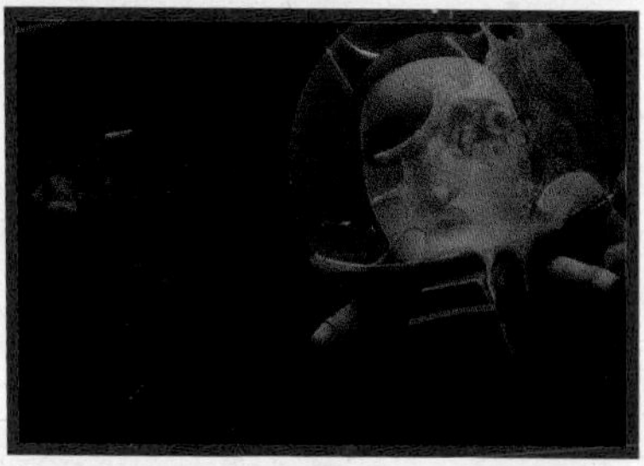
C

D

Answers: 1. Ackbar is a Mon Cala 2. Riff Tamson murdered King Yos Kolina 3. Hydroid Medusas look like jellyfish 4. He seals the crack with a blob of spit
The correct order of the scenes is A, D, B, C.